For 6–9 year olds

D1478037

My Days...
My Writings

A Journal About Me

Created by Joanne Farrell

P.O.Box 2543 • Dunnellon, FL 34430
352-615-3360
www.mymemoryjournals.com

Memory Journals for Special People

Grandma, Tell Me Your Memories
Grandpa, Tell Me Your Memories
Mom, Share Your Life With Me
Dad, Share Your Life With Me
To the Best of My Recollection
To My Dear Friend
My Days...My Pictures
My Days...My Writings
My Life...My Thoughts
Sisters
Mom, Tell Me One More Story...Your Story of Raising Me
Dad, Tell Me One More Story...Your Story of Raising Me

Distributed By:

Products

507 Industrial Street
Waverly, IA 50677

Printed in the U.S.A.
by G&R Publishing Co.

ISBN-13: 978-1-56383-055-6
ISBN-10: 1-56383-055-8
Item #5056

To the Author

The book you hold in your hands
can help record the story of you and your world.

By filling in the pages,
you will change this book into a time machine.
Someday, whether you are 25 or 75,
you'll be able to travel back in time
and remember your vacation trips,
the fights and fun with your friends,
your worst hair day,
special times with your family, and much more.

Now, before you are another day older,
start recording history –

the history of you!

The Owner and Author of this book is

_____

Age_____

Date Begun _____

Date Finished _____

This book is dedicated
to all young authors,
and to the preservation of
their very important memories...

Draw a picture of yourself. Around your picture, write words which tell things you like to do.

Today's date_____

If you were taller, what would you like to do that you can't do now?

What is your favorite food to fix for yourself?

Tell how you fix it.

Today's date_____

What are five things your mom or dad would never let you bring into the house?

Today's date_____

_____

_____

_____

_____

_____

_____

_____

_____

Tell about a nickname your friends call you. **Today's date**_____

How did you get it?

_____

_____

_____

_____

Tell about a nickname your family calls you. How did you get it? _____

_____

_____

_____

_____

How tall are you?

_____

_____

_____

How much do you weigh? _____

_____

_____

_____

_____

Where do you like to go to be by yourself?

What do you do there? _____

Draw and label your family, including pets.

Tell about the car you would like to have when you grow up.

*Today's date*_____

What will you do on the first day you can drive? _____

On this page, make a sample of your very best handwriting. To do that, you can write the alphabet or write anything you want.

*Today's date*_____

Who is your best friend(s) now?

What do you like to do together?

*Today's date*_____

_____

_____

_____

_____

_____

_____

_____

_____

_____

What does your family like to do during big snow or rain storms?

_____

_____

_____

_____

_____

_____

_____

_____

_____

Describe a time when you were very responsible.

Who is your doctor?

Tell about a memorable hospital or doctor visit.

Today's date_____

Today the temperature outside is _____.   *Today's date*_____

Draw a picture of the way it looks outside today.

*Today's date*_____

Favorites

My favorite music group is _____

My favorite color is _____

My favorite board game is _____
I like to play it with _____

My favorite outside game is _____
I like to play it with _____

My favorite place to read is _____

Write a story your grandpa told you.

_____
_____
_____
_____
_____
_____
_____
_____
_____

Draw a picture of your favorite way to cool off in the summer.

Today's date_____

If someone takes care of you while mom or dad is
gone at work, tell who it is. Tell about what you do.

*Today's date*_____

If <u>you</u> were the teacher, what would you do differently?

If you belong to a group like Girl or Boy Scouts, tell what your favorite activities are.

Today's date_____

_____

_____

_____

_____

_____

_____

_____

_____

_____

What is something you would like to get better at doing this year?

*Today's date*_____

Tell about the best surprise you ever had.

What would you do if Mom or Dad left you home alone for a week?

Today's date_____

_____

_____

_____

_____

_____

_____

_____

_____

What is a saying or word that is popular now? _____

_____

What is a popular hairstyle for girls? _____

_____

What is a popular hairstyle for boys? _____

_____

What kind of music is most popular? _____

_____

Describe or draw some popular clothes.

This summer I want to learn to...

_____

_____

_____

_____

_____

_____

_____

_____

_____

What would your mom or dad say you do best?

_____
_____
_____
_____
_____
_____
_____
_____
_____

How do you think you will earn money when you are in high school?

More Favorites

What is your favorite art activity? _____

_____

What is your favorite thing that you own? _____

_____

What is your favorite movie? _____

_____

My favorite kind of dessert is _____

_____

What is your favorite restaurant? _____

_____

What is your favorite restaurant food? _____

_____

What do you fight about with your brothers or sisters?

What happens to you when you fight with your brothers or sisters? _____

Tell about something you like to collect or another hobby you have.

*Today's date*_____

Today's date_____

My best subject is school is _____

because… _____

_____

_____

My worst subject is school is _____

because… _____

_____

_____

What are the latest things that have been happening in space exploration?

Today's date_____

How many teeth have you lost?

_____

_____

_____

_____

Tell an interesting story about losing a tooth. _____

_____

_____

_____

_____

What was the first car your mom ever drove?

What was your mom's favorite song in high school? (Maybe she will sing it to you.)

Describe or draw the styles of clothes your mom and her friends wore in high school.

Draw the kinds of telephones you have in your house now.

Today's date_____

Tell about a birthday that you enjoyed.

Tell about some things you would do if <u>you</u> were a mom or dad.

*Today's date*_____

In swimming, I'm good at _____. *Today's date*_____

Games I like to play in the water are…

_____

_____

_____

_____

_____

_____

_____

_____

_____

What is in the news a lot right now?

_____

_____

_____

_____

_____

_____

_____

_____

_____

If your family could go anywhere you wanted on a vacation, where would you go?

Today's date_____

What would you do on that vacation?_____

Draw or tell about the first house in which you remember living.

*Today's date*_____

Tell about a camping or outdoor adventure you had.

_____

_____

_____

_____

_____

_____

_____

_____

_____

What was the first thing with wheels that you could ride by yourself?

What was the very <u>worst</u> school lunch you've had?

_____

_____

_____

_____

Make a menu of your favorite school lunch food. _____

_____

_____

_____

_____

What do you like to do when there's snow on the ground? (If you live where it doesn't snow, tell what you think it would be like to live in a snowy area.)

Today's date_____

I feel the most grown-up when…

_____

_____

_____

_____

_____

_____

_____

_____

_____

What do Grandma and Grandpa let you do
that Mom and Dad don't?

*Today's date*_____

How old were you when you learned to ride a bike?

_____

_____

How did you learn to ride it? _____

_____

_____

_____

How far from home are you allowed to ride your bike by yourself? _____

_____

_____

_____

Where is a special nature place you like to go?

_____

_____

_____

_____

_____

_____

_____

_____

Draw what you think space vehicles will look like when you are an adult.

Today's date_____

My dad drives me crazy when he...

_____

_____

_____

_____

My dad makes me happy when he... _____

_____

_____

_____

_____

If you could design a backyard any way you wanted, **Today's date**_____

what would be in it? Draw and label a map to show what it would look like.

Draw and label the car(s) your family has right now.

Who is your hero?

Tell why that person is your hero.

Tell about your worst hair day.

*Today's date*_____

The scariest thing I've ever done is…

*Today's date*_____

Who is President of the United States right now?

_____

_____

_____

_____

What would you do if <u>you</u> were the President? _____

_____

_____

_____

_____

What is the best birthday present you ever
received, and who gave it to you?

Today's date_____

_____
_____
_____
_____
_____
_____
_____
_____
_____
_____

*Today's date*_____

Tell something your friends think you do really well.

_____

_____

_____

_____

_____

_____

_____

_____

_____

What are some of the newest inventions that you know about?

_____

_____

_____

_____

_____

_____

_____

_____

_____

What does Mom or Dad do to help you when you are sick? Do they have a favorite medicine they like to give you?

Today's date_____

_____

_____

_____

_____

_____

_____

_____

_____

Tell about the neighbors that live around you.

What was the first kind of car your grandma ever drove?

What was the first kind of car your grandpa ever drove? _____

Describe or draw what you would do to your
room if you could fix it up any way you wanted.

What do you think will be great about being an adult?

_____

_____

_____

_____

What do you think you will worry about most when you are an adult? _____

_____

_____

_____

_____

Who do you talk to on the phone the most?

_____

_____

_____

_____

What do you talk about? _____

_____

_____

_____

_____

How many states have you visited or lived in?

List them here.

Today's date_____

*Today's date*_____

How did your parents choose your first name?

_____

_____

_____

Your middle name? _____

_____

_____

What other names did your parents almost choose for you? _____

_____

_____

_____

What do you do while riding in the car?

During this school year I want to learn to…

_____

_____

_____

_____

_____

_____

_____

_____

_____

What do you think school desks will look like in 50 years?

Today's date_____

_____

_____

_____

_____

_____

_____

_____

_____

_____

If you have ever moved to a different house, tell about the move.

Today's date_____

Draw and tell about a machine you think someone should invent.

Today's date_____

Do you have a job for which you are paid?

What was the first car your dad ever drove?

What was your dad's favorite song in high school? (Maybe he will sing it to you.)

Describe or draw the styles of clothes your dad and his friends wore in high school.

Today's date_____

What is a good book a teacher has read to you?

_____

_____

_____

Why do you like that book? _____

_____

_____

_____

_____

Describe or draw your family's television(s).

What is the hardest word you learned
to read this year?

Today's date_____

_____

_____

_____

_____

What is the hardest math problem you can do? _____

_____

_____

_____

_____

What does your family talk about most at the
supper table?

*Today's date*_____

Before you started school last fall, what was your biggest worry about it?

*Today's date*_____

_____

_____

_____

_____

_____

_____

_____

_____

_____

What is the <u>best</u> part about going on errands
with Mom or Dad?

*Today's date*_____

_____

_____

_____

_____

_____

_____

_____

_____

_____

What is the first thing you like to do when spring finally comes?

*Today's date*_____

_____
_____
_____
_____
_____
_____
_____
_____
_____

What is something you have accomplished
that was really hard to do?

*Today's date*_____

Today's date_____

What did your grandpa(s) do for fun in the summer?

_____

_____

_____

_____

What did your grandma(s) do for fun in the summer?_____

_____

_____

_____

_____

Did you ever form a club with your friends?

_____

_____

_____

_____

What was the name of your club, and what did you do when you met? _____

_____

_____

_____

_____

How do you get your spending money?

_____

_____

_____

What do you do with your money? _____

_____

_____

_____

_____

Today's date_____

What actor or actress do you think looks most like you?

_____

_____

_____

What movie character is most like you? Tell why. _____

_____

_____

_____

_____

Tell about Mom's job(s).

_____

_____

_____

_____

What does Mom like to do when she's not working? _____

_____

_____

_____

_____

Draw a picture of your room as it looks today.

Tell what happens when you do something wrong at home.

*Today's date*_____

Tell about a concert or play you have seen.

_____

_____

_____

_____

_____

_____

_____

_____

_____

What do you think is the best age to be? Why?

Today's date_____

Tell about Dad's job(s).

What does Dad like to do when he's not working? _____

*Today's date*_____

Describe the best project you did for school this year.

_____
_____
_____
_____
_____
_____
_____
_____

*Today's date*_____

More Favorites

What is your favorite sport to play? _____

_____

What is your favorite TV commercial? _____

_____

What is your least favorite TV commercial? _____

_____

What is your favorite color? _____

_____

What is your favorite candy bar, and how much does it cost? _____

_____

Describe your mom.

Describe your dad.

Tell about your favorite place to do homework.

Why do you like to work there?

*Today's date*_____

_____

_____

_____

_____

_____

_____

_____

_____

Tell about your best vacation trip.

_____

_____

_____

_____

_____

_____

_____

_____

_____

Tell about a time when you were stung by wasps, bees, or mosquitoes.

*Today's date*_____

In school I am good at...

_____

_____

_____

_____

At recess I like to... _____

_____

_____

_____

_____

The bravest thing I ever did was...

_____

_____

_____

_____

_____

_____

_____

_____

Tell about a dream you remember.

What does your family do to help keep the earth clean?

_____

_____

_____

_____

_____

_____

_____

_____

_____

Draw an invention that would help with recycling.

What is the best thing about going shopping with Grandma and Grandpa?

Today's date_____

Today's date_____

What grade are you in this year?

_____

Who is your teacher? _____

_____

_____

Describe him or her. _____

_____

_____

_____

_____

_____

What is a tool or appliance you wish you were allowed to use? Why?

Today's date_____

Share an experience you had, or tell about your favorite ride, at a carnival, fair, or theme park.

*Today's date*_____

What mountains or big hills have you visited?

What did you do there?

*Today's date*_____

_____

_____

_____

_____

_____

_____

_____

_____

Today's date_____

What is a naughty thing you have done?

Tell about a considerate thing you have done. _____

Tell about your very first day of kindergarten.

My favorite job at home is…

_____

_____

_____

_____

My <u>least</u> favorite job at home is… _____

_____

_____

_____

_____

Who do you sit by in school?

_____

_____

Who would you <u>like</u> to sit by in school? _____

_____

_____

Why would you like to sit by that person? _____

_____

_____

_____

What book character would you most like for a friend? Why?

_____

_____

_____

_____

_____

_____

_____

_____

_____

My dad is always telling me to…

_____

_____

_____

_____

My mom is always telling me to… _____

_____

_____

_____

_____

*Today's date*_____

Tell about your favorite toy and where you got it.

_____

_____

_____

_____

_____

_____

_____

_____

_____

If I were the principal of my school, I would...

_____

_____

_____

_____

_____

_____

_____

_____

If you could have any animal for a pet, what would you want?

*Today's date*_____

What would you do if you had that pet? _____

Tell about an imaginary friend you have had.
Mom or Dad may be able to help you with this.

*Today's date*_____

Draw and label a fort, playhouse, or tree house
you made. Draw yourself in it, doing what you like to do there.

*Today's date*_____

How do you get to school each day?

_____

_____

_____

_____

_____

_____

_____

_____

Tell about your desk or table at school.

_____
_____
_____
_____
_____
_____
_____
_____
_____

*Today's date*_____

I like it when my grandpa…

_____

_____

_____

_____

I like it when my grandma… _____

_____

_____

_____

_____

*Today's date*_____

What famous person would you like to meet?

_____

_____

What would you ask or say to him or her? _____

_____

_____

_____

_____

_____

_____

A rule we should have at our house is…

_____
_____
_____
_____
_____
_____
_____
_____
_____

More Favorites

What is your favorite campfire food? _____

_____

What is your favorite board game, and who plays it with you? _____

_____

What is your favorite outside game to play? _____

_____

What is your favorite place to be alone? _____

_____

What is your favorite store to visit? _____

_____

What video or computer game or equipment is popular now?

*Today's date*_____

_____
_____
_____
_____
_____
_____
_____
_____
_____

After school I like to…

The best thing my grandma cooks for me is…

_____

_____

_____

_____

_____

_____

_____

_____

Today ask your teacher to write about something you are doing well at school.

*Today's date*_____

Write some of the words to your favorite song.

_____

_____

_____

_____

_____

_____

_____

_____

*Today's date*_____

Tell about a favorite aunt.

_____

_____

_____

_____

Tell about a favorite uncle. _____

_____

_____

_____

_____

_____

I am really curious about…

Today's date_____

What is a phrase you say often? (Someone else
may be able to help on this.)

*Today's date*_____

_____

_____

_____

_____

_____

_____

_____

_____

What do you want to be when you grow up?

_____

_____

_____

_____

Why would you be good at that job? _____

_____

_____

_____

_____

I really like it when my teacher…

_____

_____

_____

My teacher makes me mad when… _____

_____

_____

_____

_____

Mom and I have fun when we…

_____

_____

_____

Dad and I have fun when we… _____

_____

_____

_____

_____

Tell about any broken bones or injuries you've had.

What countries did your ancestors come from?

What is something you will never say to your
own children?

*Today's date*_____

My favorite teacher was…

_____

_____

_____

_____

That teacher was my favorite because… _____

_____

_____

_____

_____

My favorite place to swim is…

_____
_____
_____
_____
_____
_____
_____
_____
_____

Make a list of words that describes how your room looks right now.

*Today's date*_____

My favorite thing to do with my sister or brother is…

_____

_____

_____

_____

_____

_____

_____

_____

The naughtiest kid in my class is…

_____

_____

_____

_____

What does he or she do that is naughty? _____

_____

_____

_____

_____

If you suddenly became an adult, what would you do first?

*Today's date*_____

_____

_____

_____

_____

_____

_____

_____

_____

_____

What is the newest invention you have in your house?

You get a day off! Now it's Mom's turn. Have her tell   *Today's date*_____

about something funny you did or said when you were little.

_____

_____

_____

_____

_____

_____

_____

_____

Where would you like to be living 20 years from now? Why?

_____

_____

_____

_____

_____

_____

_____

_____

_____

Tell about a time you stayed in a cottage, hotel, or motel.

Today's date_____

What household chores did your grandma do when she was your age?

What household chores did your grandpa do when he was your age? _____

Tell about an experience using roller skates, roller blades, or a skateboard.

*Today's date*_____

_____

_____

_____

_____

_____

_____

_____

_____

_____

*Today's date*_____

More Favorites

What is your favorite pop or soda? _____

_____

The best kind of ice cream is _____

_____

My favorite cousin is _____

_____

When we're together, we like to _____

_____

What is your favorite TV show? _____

_____

What is your <u>least</u> favorite veggie? _____

_____

Tell what you know about the day you were born.

You might have to ask someone to help you.

*Today's date*_____

If you've ever ridden on a train or plane, tell about it.

What do you think you and your brothers and
sisters will do together when you all grow up?

*Today's date*_____

_____
_____
_____
_____
_____
_____
_____
_____
_____

What household chores did your mom have to do when she was your age?

Today's date_____

What household chores did your dad have to do when he was your age? _____

Draw the kind of house you would like to live in when you grow up.

Today's date_____

My favorite thing my mom does is…

_____

_____

_____

My favorite thing my dad does is… _____

_____

_____

_____

_____

You get a day off! Now it's Dad's turn. Have him tell about something funny you did or said when you were little.

*Today's date*_____

_____
_____
_____
_____
_____
_____
_____
_____

What relative's or friend's house do you most enjoy visiting?

*Today's date*_____

Tell about what you do while you're there. _____

Describe your favorite pair of shoes.

Tell about something your brother or sister can do well.

_____

_____

_____

_____

_____

_____

_____

_____

_____

Tell about a favorite toy you've had since you were a baby.

*Today's date*_____

*Today's date*_____

Tell about the best book you ever read.

_____

_____

_____

_____

_____

_____

_____

_____

_____

If I could have a special magic wish for someone else, I would wish...

*Today's date*_____

_____
_____
_____
_____
_____
_____
_____
_____
_____

Holidays

If these holiday pages do not pertain to your family, you can remove this section or change the questions to reflect your holidays and traditions.

My New Year's resolutions for this year are…

_____

_____

_____

_____

_____

_____

_____

_____

_____

What did you do to celebrate Valentine's Day?

_____

_____

_____

_____

_____

_____

_____

_____

My family celebrates Easter by...

_____

_____

_____

_____

_____

_____

_____

_____

_____

Why is the 4th of July celebrated?

_____

_____

_____

_____

_____

_____

_____

_____

Tell what you do to celebrate Halloween.

What are five things for which you are thankful?

_____

_____

_____

_____

_____

_____

_____

_____

What does your family usually do during
Thanksgiving?

*Today's date*_____

_____

_____

_____

_____

_____

_____

_____

_____

Tell how <u>you</u> would fix a turkey for dinner.

_____

_____

_____

_____

_____

_____

_____

_____

_____

Ask your mom or dad about your very first
Christmas. Write about it.

What are your favorite parts of the holiday season?

_____

_____

_____

_____

_____

_____

_____

_____

My favorite holiday food is…

I think you fix it like this: _____

How did your dad celebrate Christmas when he was your age?

*Today's date*_____

How did your mom celebrate Christmas when she was your age?

*Today's date*_____

Tell about some of your favorite holiday memories.

You have just authored a book. Congratulations! *Today's date*_____

You may design your own completion certificate telling what date you started,
what date you finished, how old you are at this time, and any other "official"
information you'd like to include.

Today's date_____

Today's date_____

Today's date_____

Today's date_____

Today's date_____